Thanksgiving
Activity Book

Blue Wave Press

Coloring
Pages

HAPPY THANKSGIVING

THANKSGIVING

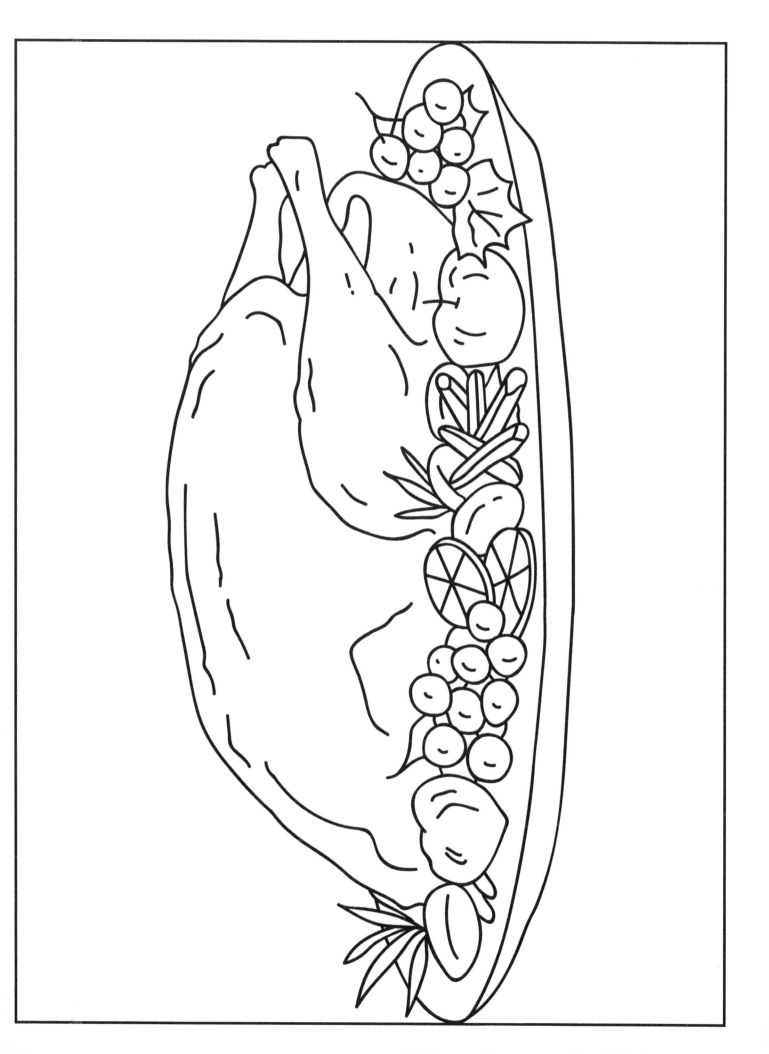

Thanksgiving Day

Thanksgiving Day

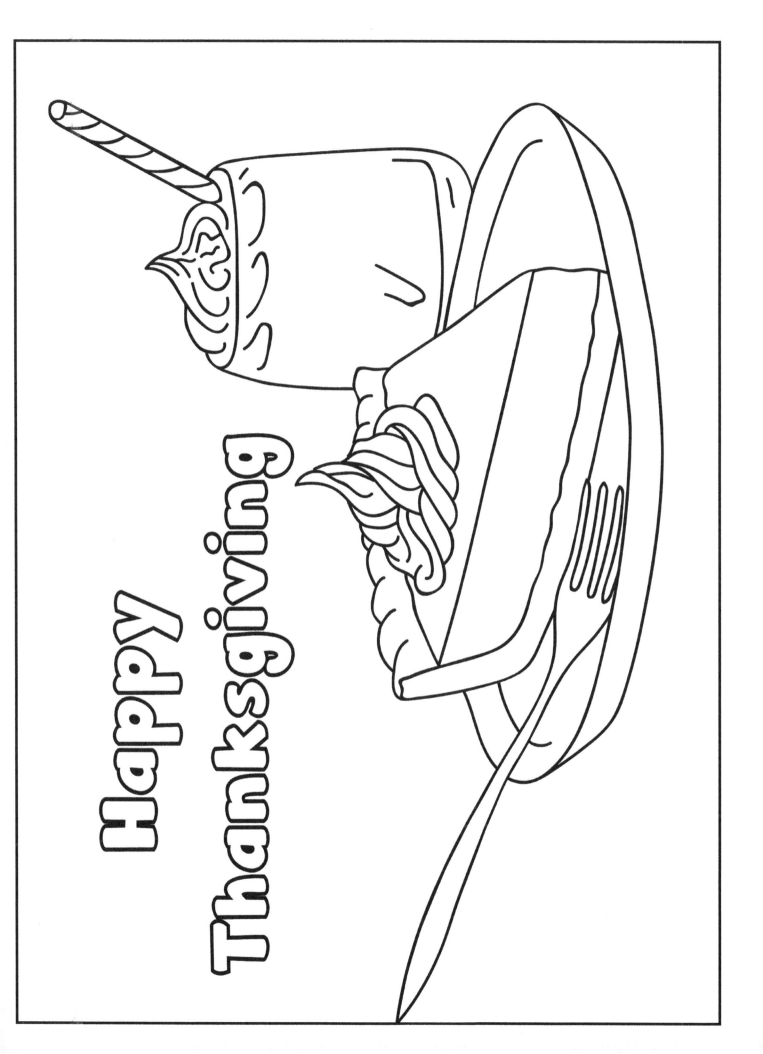

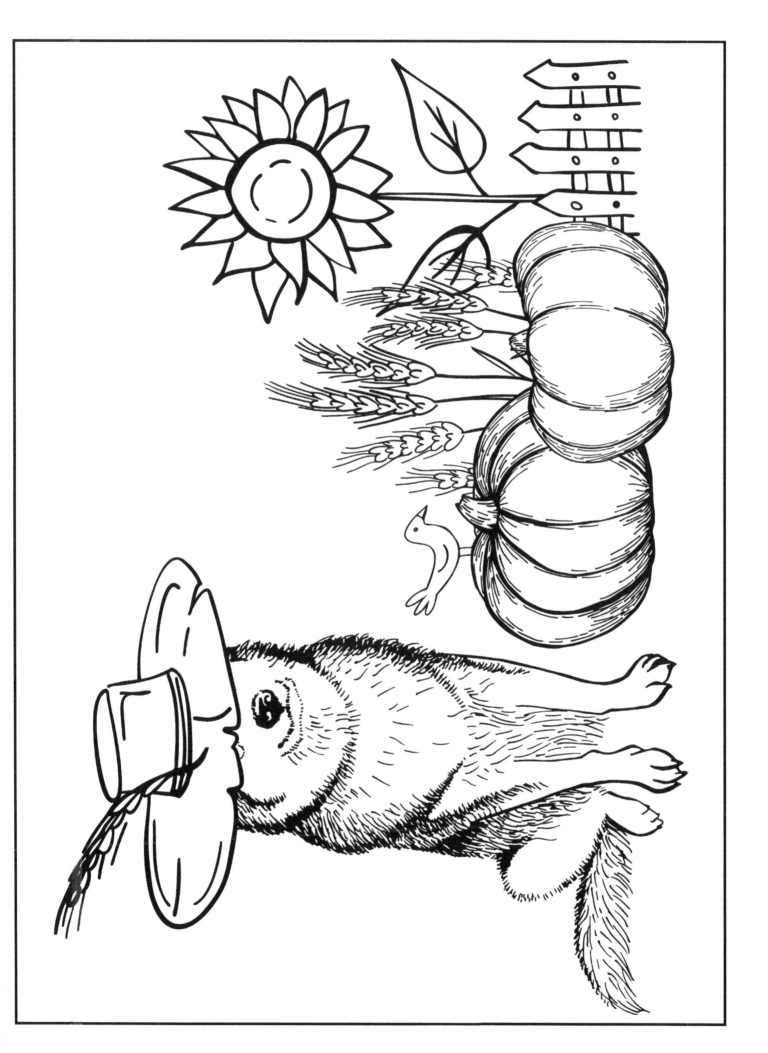

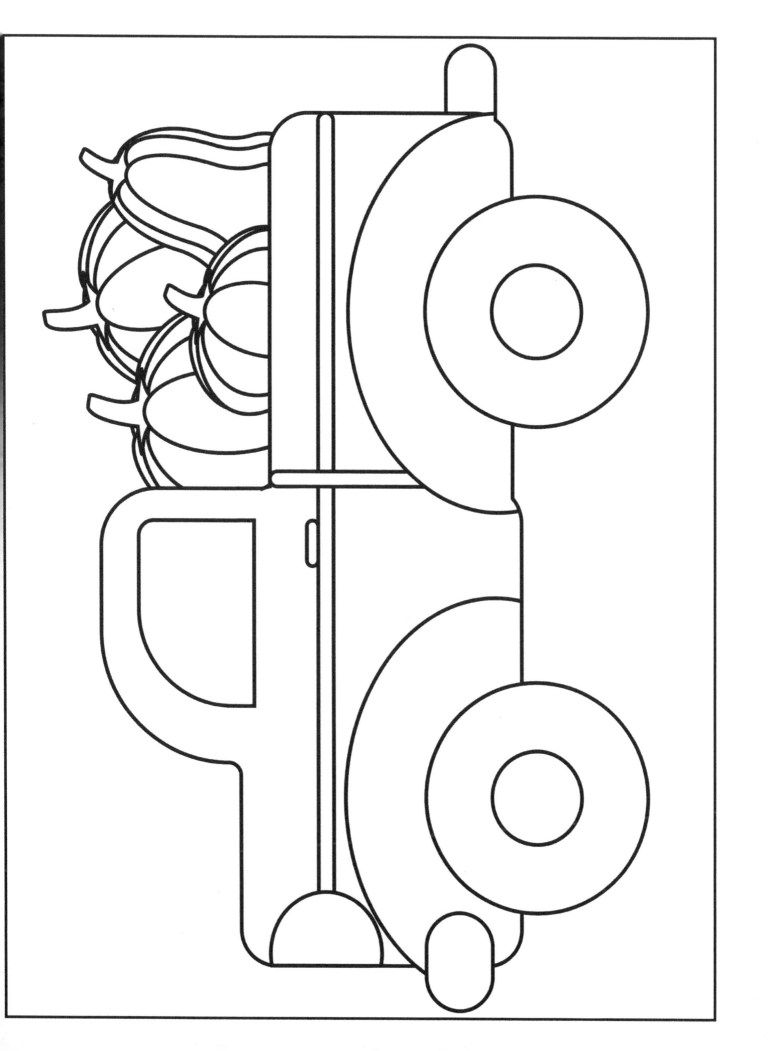

HAPPY

THANKSGIVING

Activity Pages

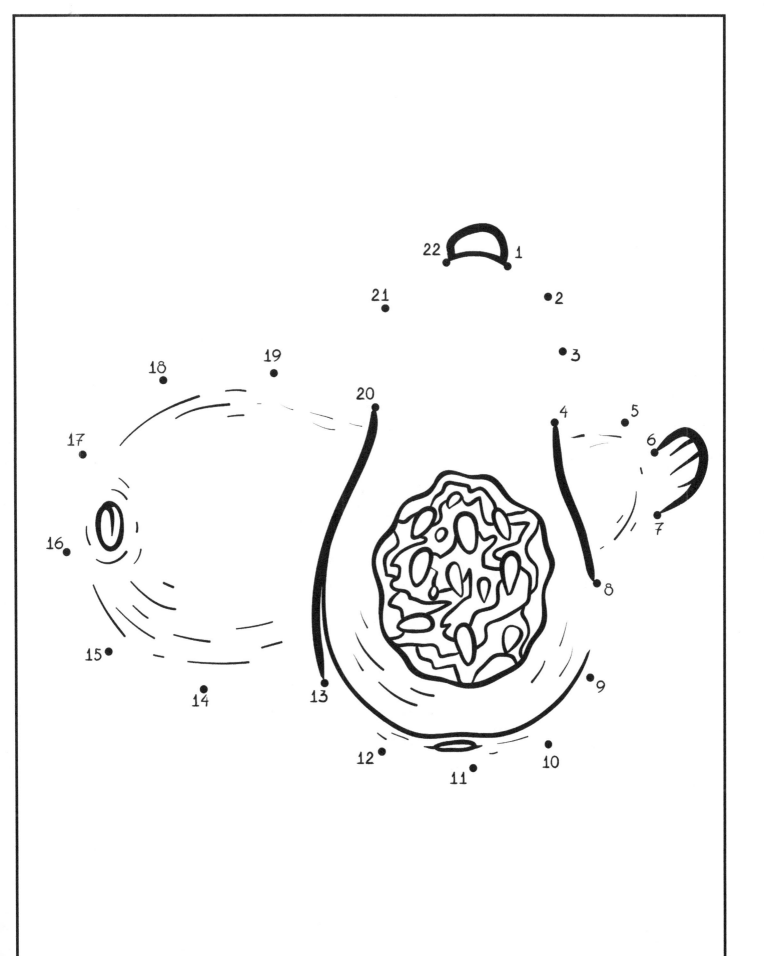

Find the Words

P	U	M	P	K	I	N	H	K	A
T	A	M	Y	M	E	L	A	O	C
E	T	U	R	K	E	Y	R	A	R
A	K	P	O	N	D	A	V	J	A
M	A	Y	F	L	O	W	E	R	N
P	U	M	R	M	O	N	S	I	B
I	T	O	A	I	L	E	T	S	E
L	U	P	I	L	G	R	I	M	R
G	M	I	N	A	K	M	E	B	R
M	N	N	O	P	I	E	L	E	Y

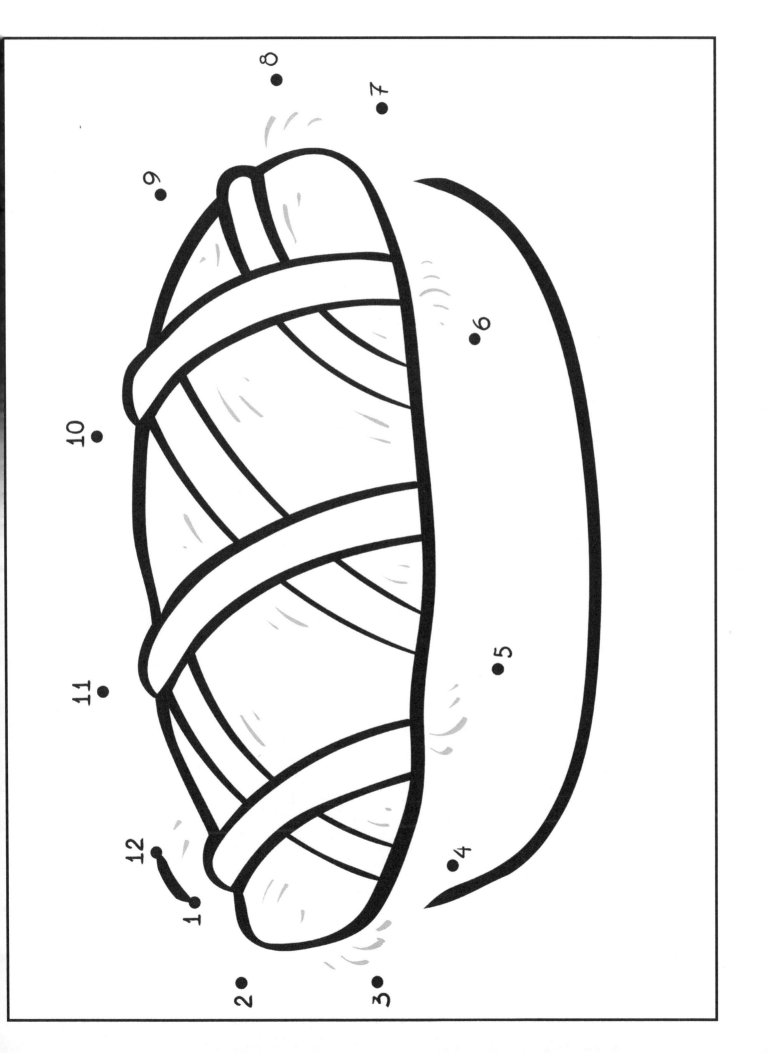

Find the Words

H	H	A	P	P	L	E	S	Q	P
A	C	O	R	N	C	D	D	W	U
D	J	T	U	R	K	E	Y	E	M
P	E	M	J	R	H	A	T	O	P
L	P	A	A	U	T	U	M	N	K
X	I	P	D	M	H	F	Y	D	I
C	E	L	C	E	S	E	H	E	N
O	V	E	C	A	N	D	L	E	B
R	G	B	L	E	A	F	F	T	N
N	H	A	L	L	O	W	E	E	N

Help the Turkey Get the Corn

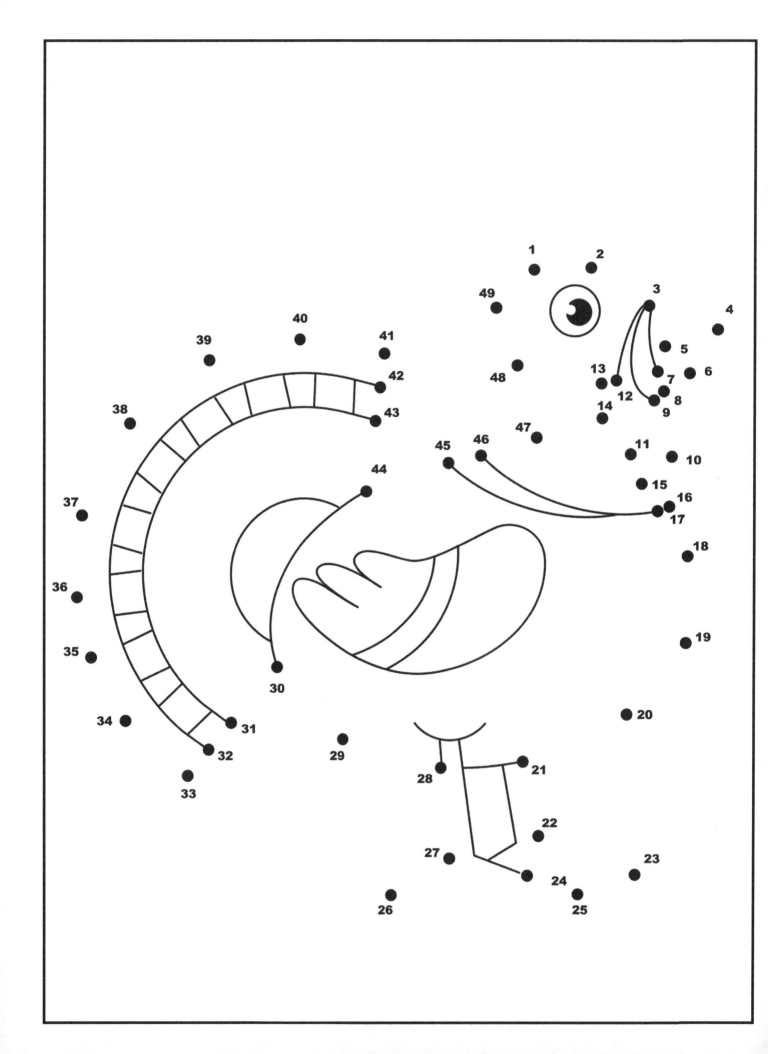

Solve the Rebus Puzzles

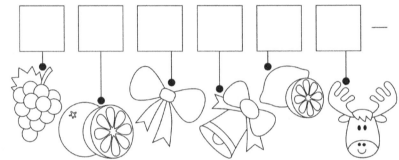

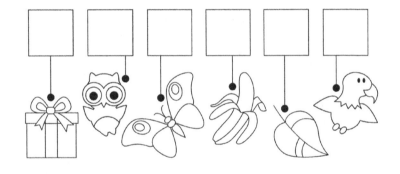

Copy the Picture Using the Grid

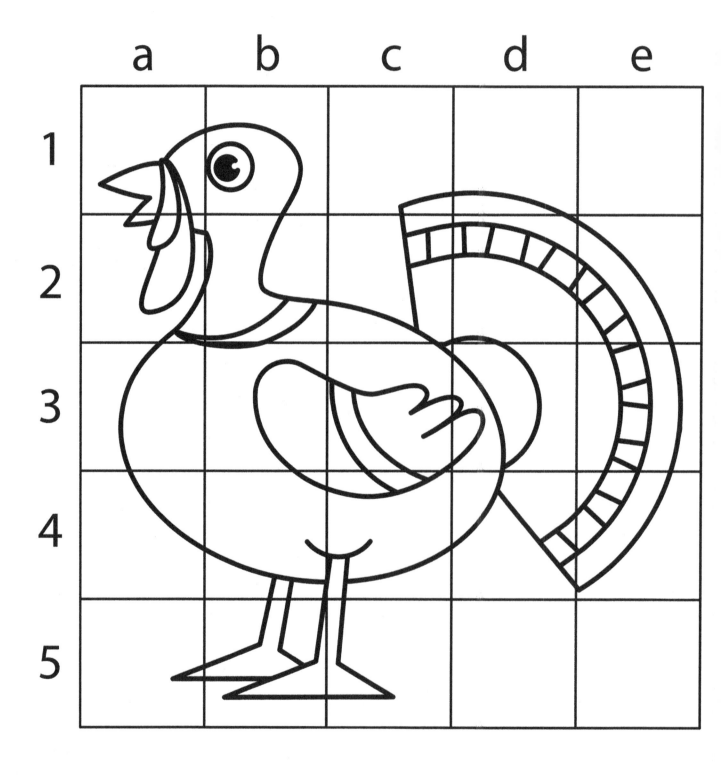

	a	b	c	d	e
1					
2					
3					
4					
5					

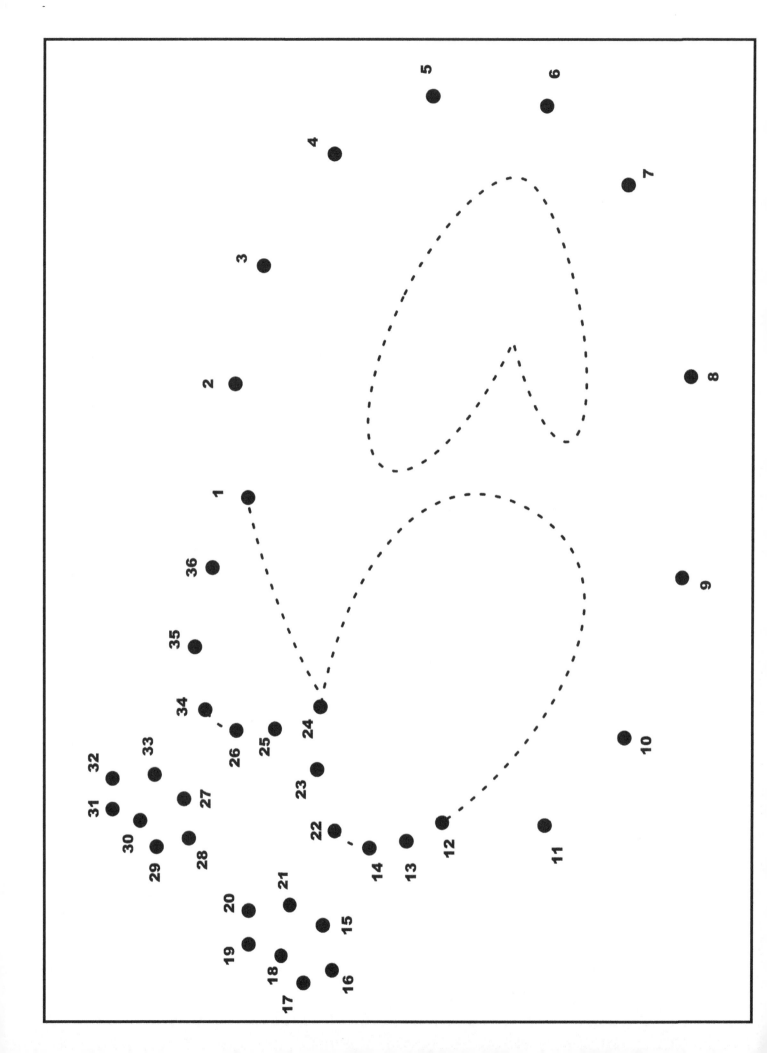

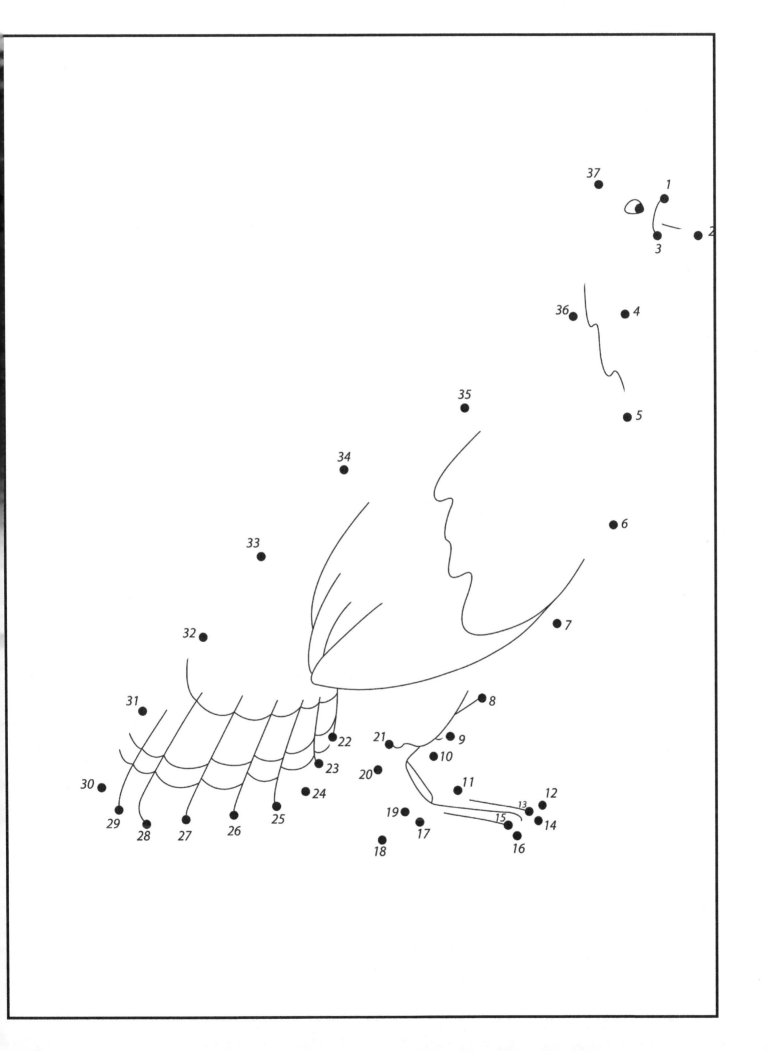

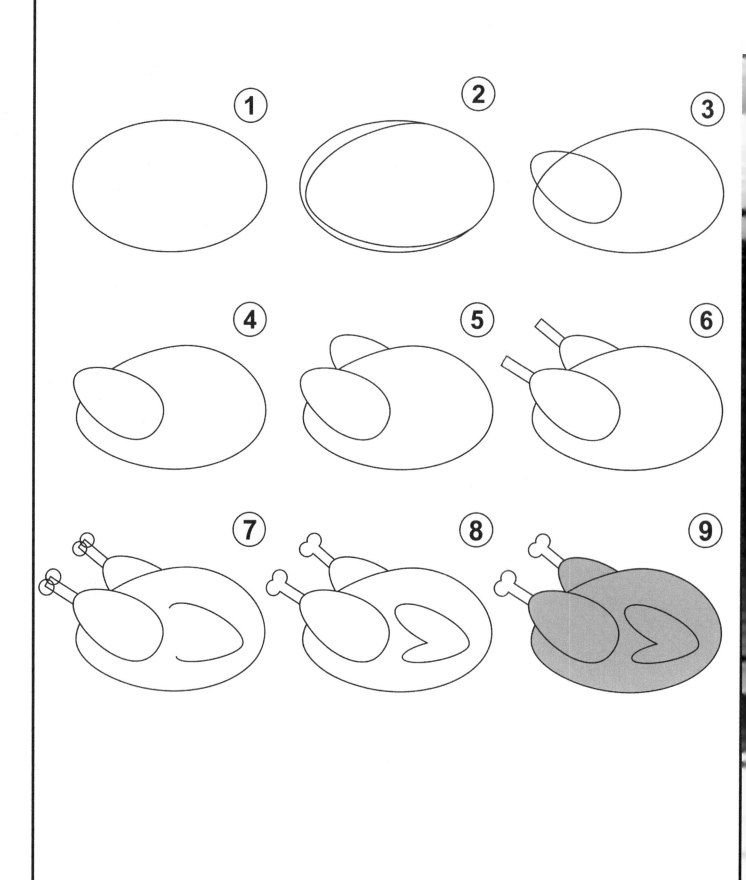

Your Turn to Draw

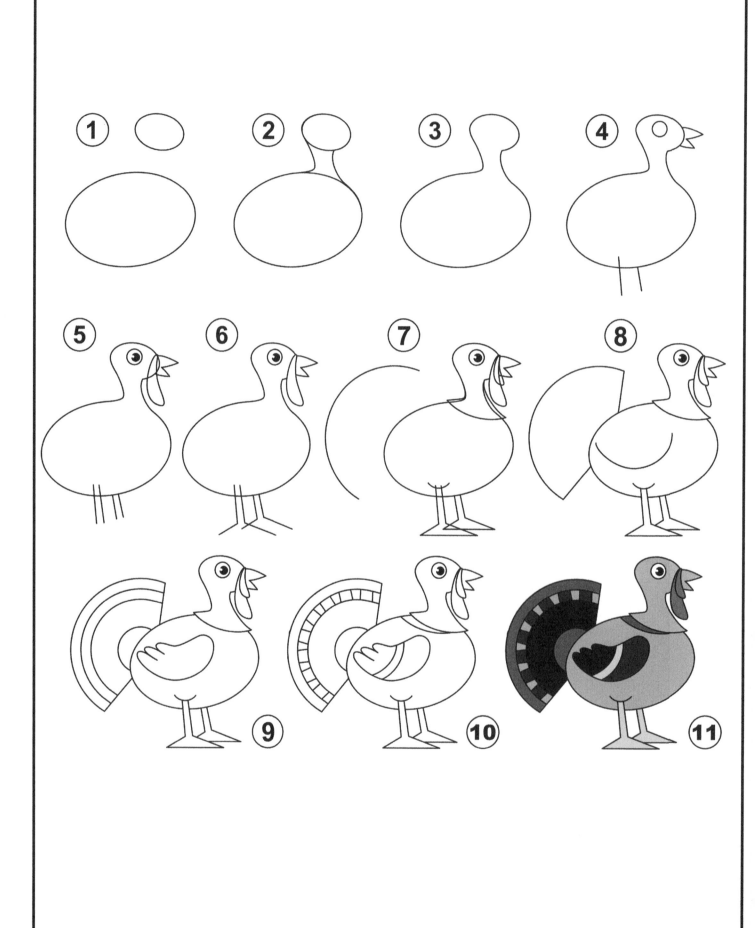

Your Turn to Draw

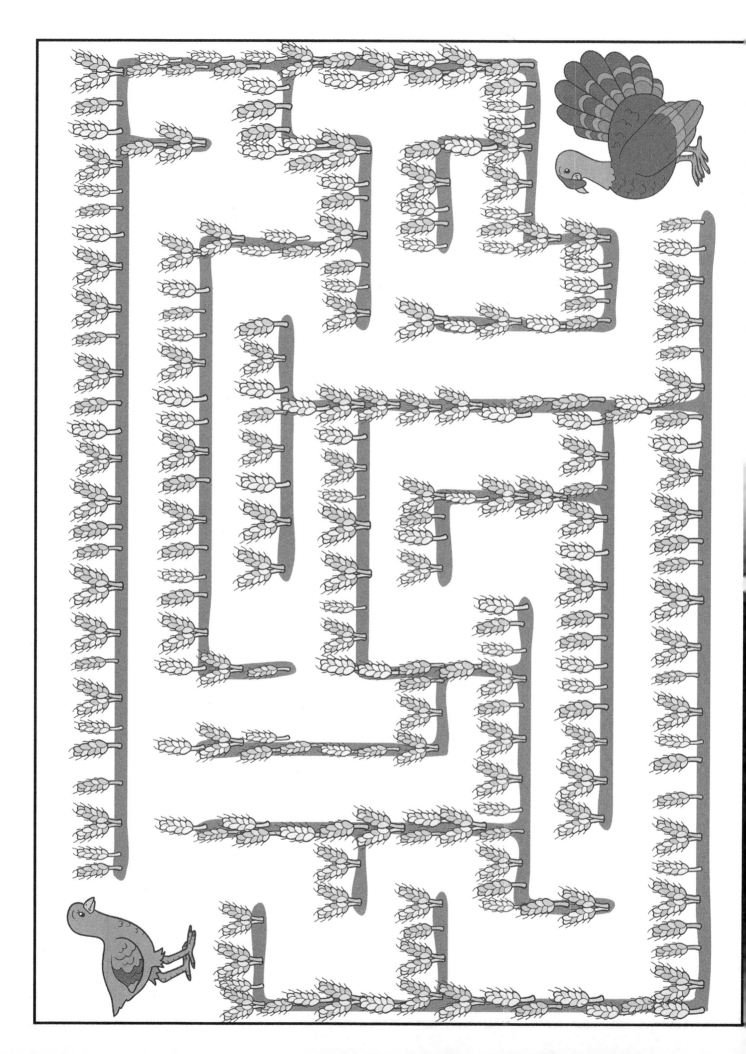

Find two of the same pictures.

1 - green
2 - light green
3 - red
4 - orange
5 - dark brown
6 - brown
7 - light brown
8 - tan
9 - dark pink

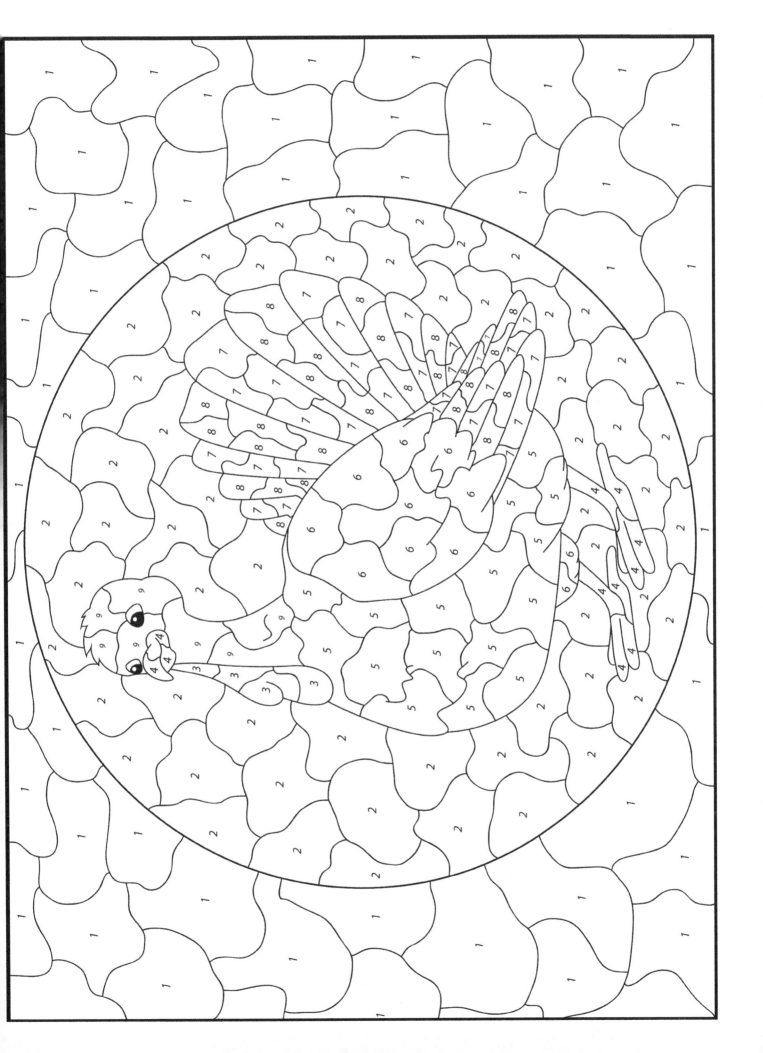

1 - green
2 - light green
3 - orange
4 - dark brown
5 - tan
6 - light brown

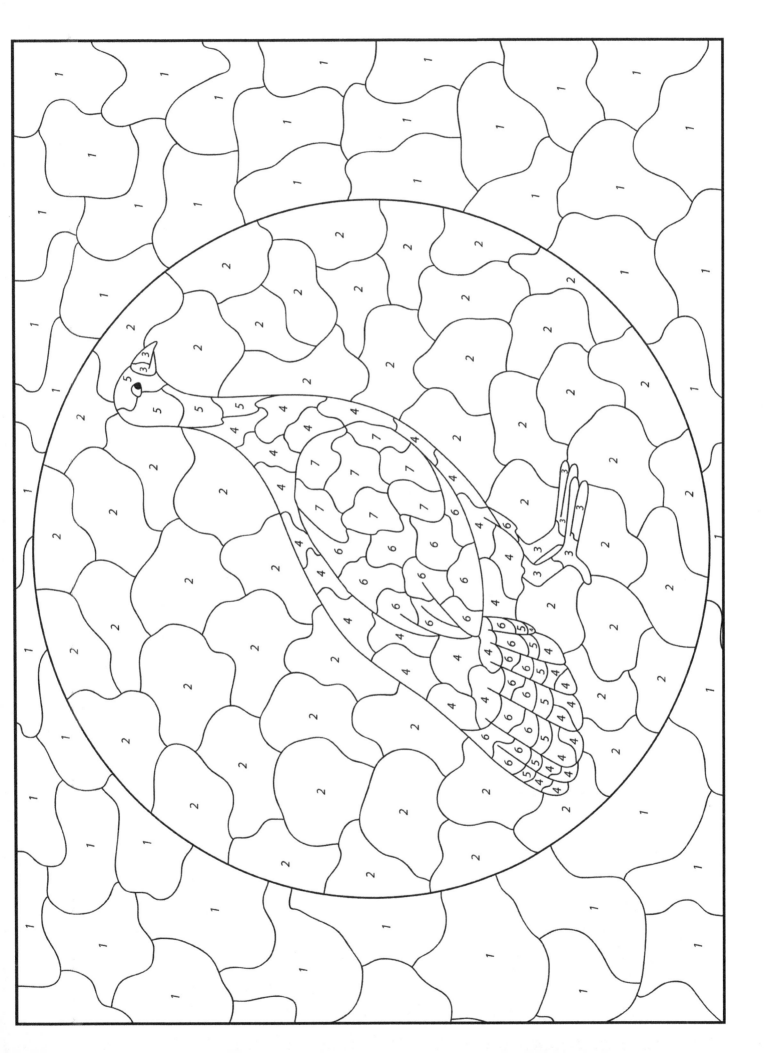

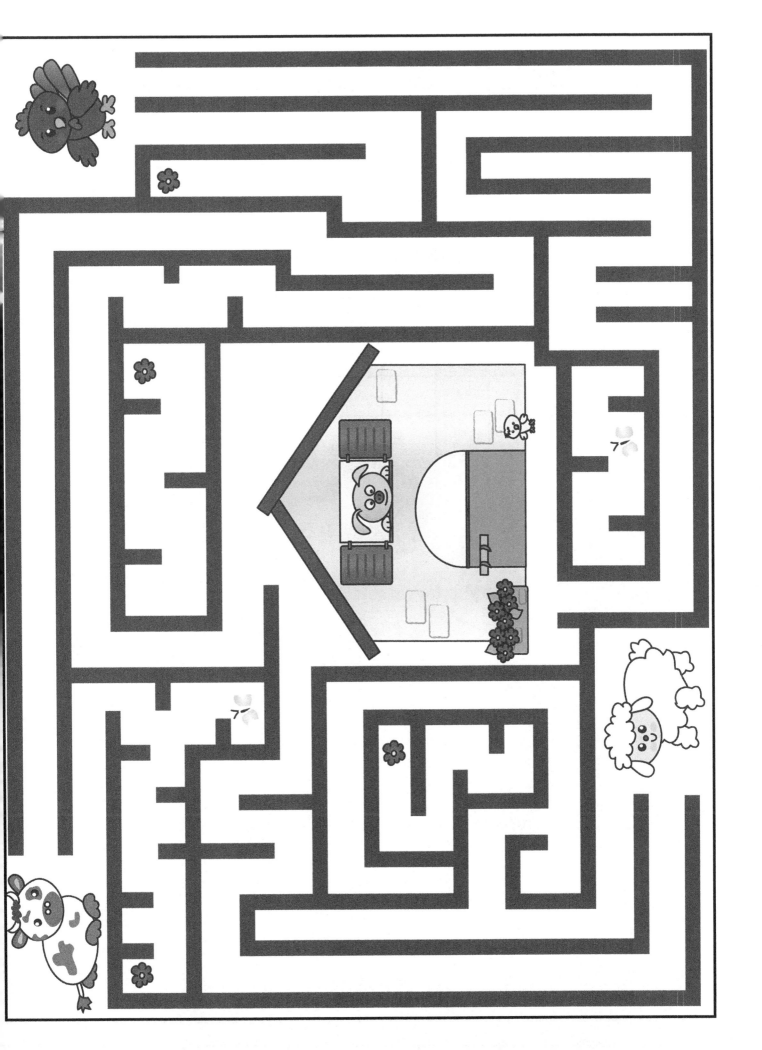

Solve for Hidden Word

Word Search

```
U G I B L E T S Q T B O
G R D J X S A E X E C Y
W E A T E T B V D M U C
C I F V O D A N E A Y G
U F A A O Q K F L I T O
I E F H L K E S I Z R V
L N Q S M L E B C E Z Q
D W D A C O X F I N U P
O N H I N S Z X O I A C
O T U A A T Z C U U X P
M T C T W N C O S R W V
A C O R N S S B M I I K
```

ACORNS   GIBLETS

BAKE   HAM

CANOE   INDIANS

DELICIOUS   LEAVES

EAT   MAIZE

FALL   NAP

Word Search

```
T G R A T I T U D E R N
L H T A M E R I C A E P
D K A C H C G F U T Q N
S C F N P O W W A J O L
E O A A K W L R M I A S
T L M P K S B I T U K M
T O I T A E G I D N Q G
L N L N L R D I A A K Y
E I Y E J A A H V O Y V
R S C A R Q T D Z I K Z
S T M T T S Q C E J N D
K S B L E S S I N G S G
```

AMERICA	HOLIDAY
BLESSINGS	PARADE
CELEBRATE	SETTLERS
COLONISTS	THANKS
FAMILY	THANKSGIVING
GRATITUDE	TRADITION

Word Search

```
C P I Z N R A P C O R N
R G E C A S S E R O L E
A F A C V Y C R O L L S
N D P Z A O U D F N G K
B B P S J N A X I I C K
E B L A Q E P N L I E Z
R D E G R U I I T B G O
R M P B C K A S E X R G
I W I F P I M S Z T A S
E T E M Y U D E H A V K
S E U Z R V V E C M Y S
T P W D R R K S R A D J
```

APPLE PIE   DRUMSTICK
BREAD   GRAVY
CASSEROLE   PECAN PIE
CIDER   PUMPKIN
CORN   ROLLS
CRANBERRIES   SQUASH

Word Search

```
R C Q N D Q R J K N F Y
S E O Q O E E R M R A S
E P Z L T D E U M E L N
A B H N D B T M Y G L O
S P I V M U D Q J M S W
O W L E A H O L I D A Y
N L V A T H U R S D A Y
S O E T N H A R V E S T
N O B A A T V C H X B J
V Z N D V C I E U M O Q
K G U O W E H N X E G X
U Z Y B C J S M G B G N
```

AUTUMN	NOVEMBER
COLD	PLANTING
FALL	SEASONS
HARVEST	SNOW
HOLIDAY	THURSDAY
LEAVES	WINTER

Word Search

```
Q A C E L E B R A T E R
N J C C P U B R W G B E
Q R I O R I U F A I D G
T F B E R T L M Z U E R
R S L H L N I G T S E L
A V E O F W U I R Y C T
D M S M F A T C A I S U
I T S E N A M R O A M G
T H I U R F P I E P N S
I M N G C U G F L N I E
O Q G P A R A D E Y V A
N A S H O L I D A Y K B
```

BLESSINGS   HOLIDAY
CELEBRATE   HOME
CORNUCOPIA   PARADE
FAMILY   PILGRIMS
FEAST   PRAYER
GRATITUDE   TRADITION

Unscramble the Words

1. IPATNALTNO

_ _ _ _ _ _ _ _ _ _

2. ETRELBACE

_ _ _ _ _ _ _ _ _

3. ESSGLBSNI

_ _ _ _ _ _ _ _ _

4. RECSOLESA

_ _ _ _ _ _ _ _ _

5. BRNCODERA

_ _ _ _ _ _ _ _ _

6. ELPAP PEI

_ _ _ _ _ _ _ _ _

7. ENEVRMBO

_ _ _ _ _ _ _ _

8. LEBBOG

_ _ _ _ _ _

9. PNKUIMP

_ _ _ _ _ _ _

10. SIERBERRNCA

_ _ _ _ _ _ _ _ _ _ _

Unscramble the Words

1. LEATLOTCBH ＿ ＿ ＿ ＿ ＿ ＿ ＿ ＿ ＿ ＿

2. LTVFREOSE ＿ ＿ ＿ ＿ ＿ ＿ ＿ ＿ ＿

3. EYRTUK ＿ ＿ ＿ ＿ ＿ ＿

4. AGVEOY ＿ ＿ ＿ ＿ ＿ ＿

5. OLMEFAWRY ＿ ＿ ＿ ＿ ＿ ＿ ＿ ＿ ＿

6. ESOSSNA ＿ ＿ ＿ ＿ ＿ ＿ ＿

7. ODAIRTTIN ＿ ＿ ＿ ＿ ＿ ＿ ＿ ＿ ＿

8. FFSGUTNI ＿ ＿ ＿ ＿ ＿ ＿ ＿ ＿

9. SVEGBLTEEA ＿ ＿ ＿ ＿ ＿ ＿ ＿ ＿ ＿ ＿

10. VGKNSIAGHNIT ＿ ＿ ＿ ＿ ＿ ＿ ＿ ＿ ＿ ＿ ＿ ＿

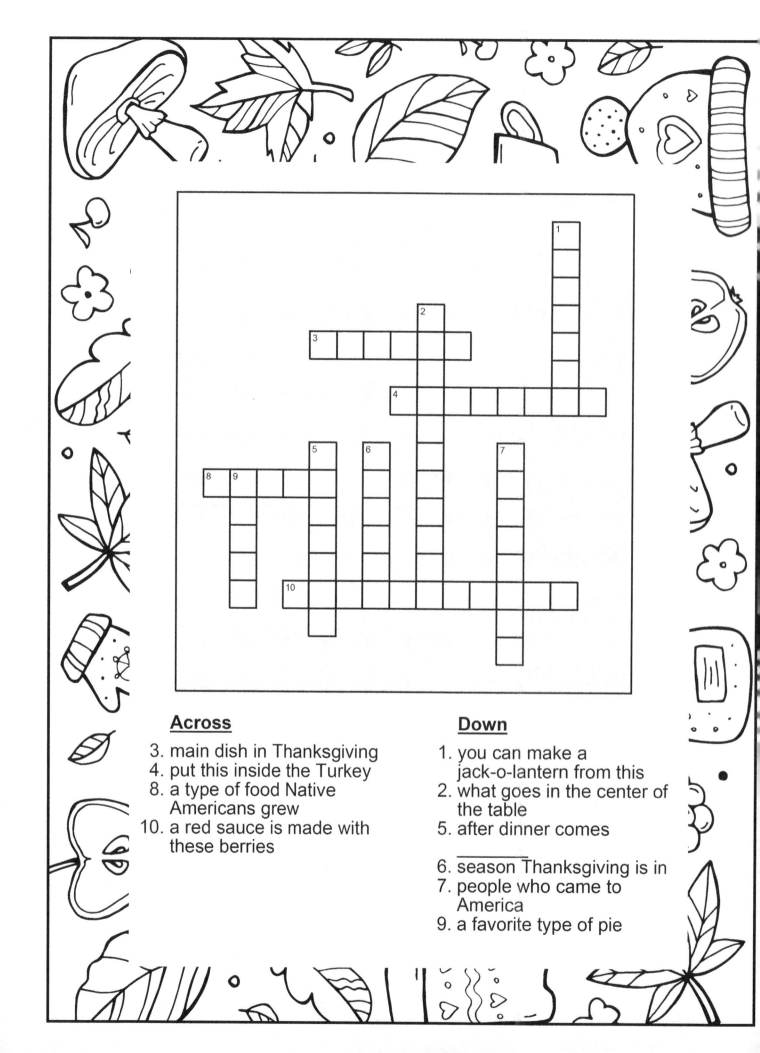

Across

3. main dish in Thanksgiving
4. put this inside the Turkey
8. a type of food Native Americans grew
10. a red sauce is made with these berries

Down

1. you can make a jack-o-lantern from this
2. what goes in the center of the table
5. after dinner comes _____
6. season Thanksgiving is in
7. people who came to America
9. a favorite type of pie

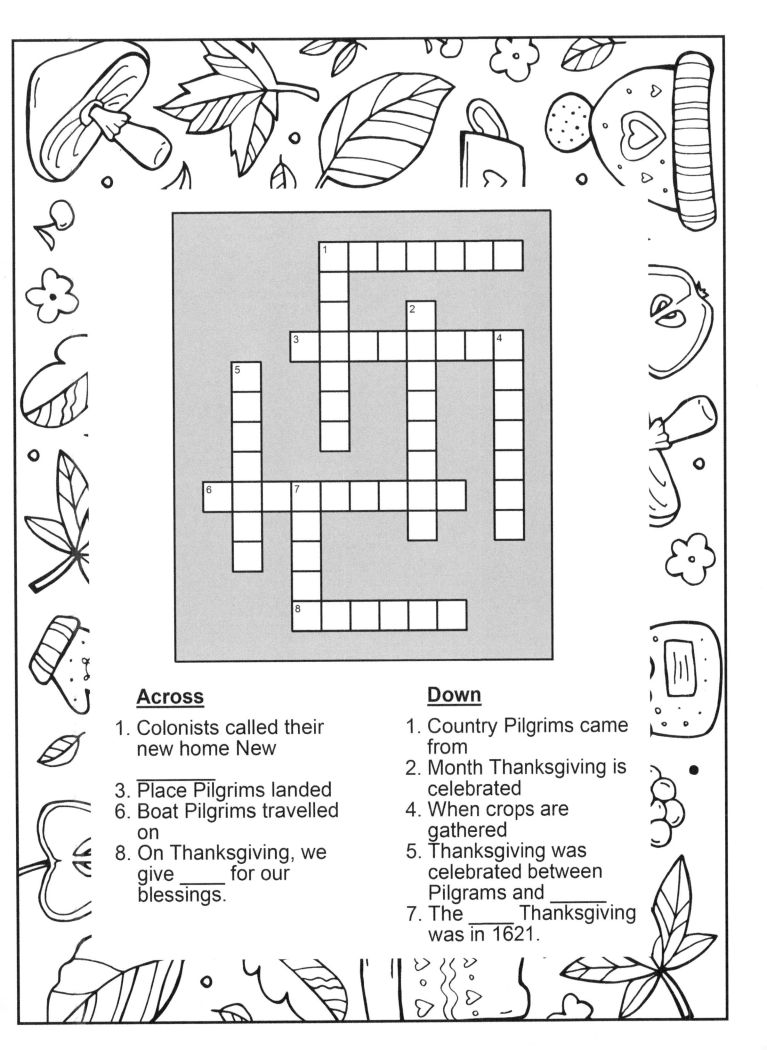

Across

1. Colonists called their new home New _____

3. Place Pilgrims landed
6. Boat Pilgrims travelled on
8. On Thanksgiving, we give ____ for our blessings.

Down

1. Country Pilgrims came from
2. Month Thanksgiving is celebrated
4. When crops are gathered
5. Thanksgiving was celebrated between Pilgrams and ____
7. The ____ Thanksgiving was in 1621.

P	U	M	P	K	I	N	H	K	A
T	A	M	Y	M	E	L	A	O	C
E	T	U	R	K	E	Y	R	A	R
A	K	P	O	N	D	A	V	J	A
M	A	Y	F	L	O	W	E	R	N
P	U	M	R	M	O	N	S	I	B
I	T	O	A	I	L	E	T	S	E
L	U	P	I	L	G	R	I	M	R
G	M	I	N	A	K	M	E	B	R
M	N	N	O	P	I	E	L	E	Y

H	H	A	P	P	L	E	S	Q	P
A	C	O	R	N	C	D	D	W	U
D	J	T	U	R	K	E	Y	E	M
P	E	M	J	R	H	A	T	O	P
L	P	A	A	U	T	U	M	N	K
X	I	P	D	M	H	F	Y	D	I
C	E	L	C	E	S	E	H	E	N
O	V	E	C	A	N	D	L	E	B
R	G	B	L	E	A	F	F	T	N
N	H	A	L	L	O	W	E	E	N

ANSWER	Gobble-gobble

ANSWER	Turkey

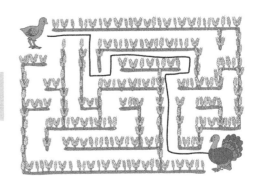

Happy Thanksgiving

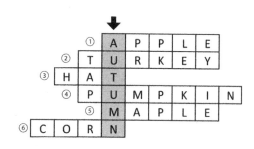

① A P P L E
② T U R K E Y
③ H A T
④ P U M P K I N
⑤ M A P L E
⑥ C O R N

ACORNS   GIBLETS
BAKE   HAM
CANOE   INDIANS
DELICIOUS   LEAVES
EAT   MAIZE
FALL   NAP

AMERICA   HOLIDAY
BLESSINGS   PARADE
CELEBRATE   SETTLERS
COLONISTS   THANKS
FAMILY   THANKSGIVING
GRATITUDE   TRADITION

APPLE PIE   DRUMSTICK
BREAD   GRAVY
CASSEROLE   PECAN PIE
CIDER   PUMPKIN
CORN   ROLLS
CRANBERRIES   SQUASH

AUTUMN   NOVEMBER
COLD   PLANTING
FALL   SEASONS
HARVEST   SNOW
HOLIDAY   THURSDAY
LEAVES   WINTER

BLESSINGS   HOLIDAY
CELEBRATE   HOME
CORNUCOPIA   PARADE
FAMILY   PILGRIMS
FEAST   PRAYER
GRATITUDE   TRADITION

1. IPATNALTNO   p l a n t a t i o n
2. ETRELBACE   c e l e b r a t e
3. ESSGLBSNI   b l e s s i n g s
4. RECSOLESA   c a s s e r o l e
5. BRNCODERA   c o r n b r e a d
6. ELPAP PEI   a p p l e   p i e
7. ENEVRMBO   N o v e m b e r
8. LEBBOG   g o b b l e
9. PNKUIMP   p u m p k i n
10. SIERBERRNCA   c r a n b e r r i e s

1. LEATLOTCBH   t a b l e c l o t h
2. LTVFREOSE   l e f t o v e r s
3. EYRTUK   t u r k e y
4. AGVEOY   v o y a g e
5. OLMEFAWRY   M a y f l o w e r
6. ESOSSNA   s e a s o n s
7. ODAIRTTIN   t r a d i t i o n
8. FFSGUTNI   s t u f f i n g
9. SVEGBLTEEA   v e g e t a b l e s
10. VGKNSIAGHNIT   t h a n k s g i v i n g

Across
3. main dish in Thanksgiving
4. put this inside the Turkey
8. a type of food Native Americans grew
10. a red sauce is made with these berries

Down
1. you can make a jack-o-lantern from this
2. what goes in the center of the table
5. after dinner comes
6. ___ season Thanksgiving is in
7. people who came to America
9. a favorite type of pie

Across
1. Colonists called their new home New ___
3. Place Pilgrims landed
6. Boat Pilgrims travelled on
8. On Thanksgiving, we give ___ for our blessings.

Down
1. Country Pilgrims came from
2. Month Thanksgiving is celebrated
4. When crops are gathered
5. Thanksgiving was celebrated between Pilgrams and ___
7. The ___ Thanksgiving was in 1621.

Made in the USA
Coppell, TX
22 November 2022